Book 1

by Lee D. Stockner

Play Challenging Songs with a Simple Language of Music

Need replacement rings?? They are available at
OccupationalOctaves.com.

© 2014 Music Lee Inclined Guy, Inc.

Printed in the U.S.A.

ISBN: 978-0-9887`04-1-2

Special Thanks

To my parents, Ruth & Steven, for always being there for me, inspiring me, and making every decision with love and family in mind. I love you both.

To my sister Lauren — 5 years younger & 5 years more mature — my best friend and closest ally in life. Our mutual belief in each other is endless

To Guy & the Brogna family, for being an irreplaceable part of this journey. There is no Occupational Octaves without you.

To Deb, Ross, and Chase Burwasser, for changing my life in an incredible and unimaginable way, sparking the chain of events that led to this book series.

To Robyn, Allan, Jamie, and Alex Schneider, for their drive as a family to defy the odds and redefine the limitations of Autism

To those who mentored, taught, advised, or inspired me: Diane Dybus, Steven Sussman, Gregg & Lisa Cohen, and my original thought leader, George Carlin.

And especially, to the thousands of students I have worked with since focusing my career on music education, and then special education. My greatest learning experience in life has been our time spent together.

Thank you.

Dear Instructors,

Welcome to Book 1 of the Occupational Octaves Piano™ curriculum! It is an honor for us here at Music Lee Inclined Guy, Inc., that you have chosen to try this approach to learning to play the piano – an entirely new language.

Occupational Octaves Piano™ utilizes an entirely new language of music, named Lee Stockner's Music Box Method™. Inside these pages you will find a series of colored letters in rhythmically designed boxes that, along with a properly labeled keyboard and our signature colored rings (#RingsOnTheFingers), function just like traditional notation. This statement refers specifically to the three main instructions of the original language of music – which note to play, which finger to use, and how long to hold for. With this adaptation, students with basic color and letter matching skills may be able to play a full classical curriculum without reading a single black and white music note. The origin of Occupational Octaves Piano™ reaches back to 2008 and there are hundreds of videos supporting this notion.

The name, Occupational Octaves Piano™, was derived from the idea that when students are no longer struggling to understand the confusing & complex original language of music (which I am personally quite proud to be able to read), the human developments that are possible at the piano become much easier to focus on. When an old friend who is also a highly accomplished occupational therapist listened to me explain what I was noticing with my students fingers, hands, eyes, posture, and more, she told me that these were all areas of improvement which an occupational therapist may seek to develop. I realized that the goals I was reaching were non-musical, while the students were highly engaged in music. This special combination led to the unique name and approach of OOP.

These realizations also led to us create a system designed to bring the piano directly into special education classrooms, music conservatories, therapeutic environments, assisted living facilities, and more. Visit OccupationalOctaves.com for more on information, research, testimonials, and much more! You can also add your name to the map of Occupational Octaves™ users, so if someone in your area is looking for an instructor who is familiar with the curriculum, you can be easily found.

Good luck with Occupational Octaves Piano™!

Lee Stockner

Lee Stockner's Music Box Method™ is a new language of music using colored letters in rhythmically designed boxes for students to read music and play countless songs. The teacher's goal and student's focus should always be understanding which note(s) to play, which finger(s) to use and how long to hold. These are the same principles as traditional notation and although the music of Occupational Octaves Piano™ doesn't look like traditional notation, it has all of the same information! Let's try it out –

Materials:

Piano/Keyboard   Dry Erase Marker   Music Box Color Rings   Occupational Octaves Bk.1

Hand/Ring/Keyboard Setup:

To begin, use your dry erase marker to draw a letter C on the note to the left of the two centermost black keys on your piano/keyboard. Take out a pink and red ring from the back of your book and open to Pg. 1, The New C. Keep your marker nearby to draw more letters on "The New" pages like The New D and The New A as you and your student progress.

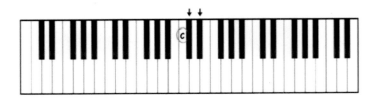

Early in this book when only pink and red C's are played, the Hand/Ring/Letters setup is simplest:

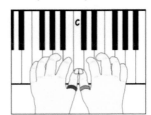

Midway through the book when 5 letters are being used, the Hand/Ring/Letters will grow, but the hands remain in place:

Here is the complete Hand/Ring/Letter setup for Lee Stockner's Music Box Method, as worn on Pg. 33 when 10 fingers are used.

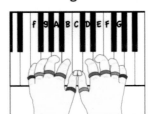

Reading Lee Stockner's Music Box Method:

This is a typical Music Box Sheet:

If you see a green D in the top box:

Press on the D with your right hand green finger:

VERY IMPORTANT NOTE - Letters in the top boxes are played with the right hand and letters in the bottom boxes are played with the left hand***

Making Music with Lee Stockner's Music Box Method:

To make music with this method, the instructor needs to help the student through a steady beat, one top and bottom box set at a time. The teacher will act much like a bouncy ball in a sing-a-long video by pointing to the colored letters as the student plays and moving along at a steady pace with each correct note played with the correct finger.

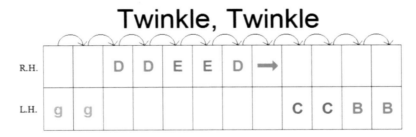

While moving along beat by beat, you'll come across some arrows that are always in the same color as the preceding letter. These arrows are "hold" arrows and they mean for your student to hold the initial note an extra beat (or pace) per arrow. The teacher should be pointing to the letters and holds while both the student and teacher say the "hold" out loud.

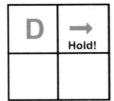

or

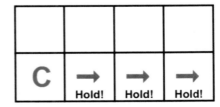

Table of Contents

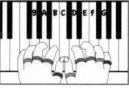

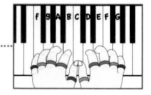

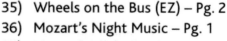

The New C

Written by Lee D. Stockner

Translated & Arranged for Occupational Octaves™ by Lee D. Stockner

C	C	C	C	C	C	C	C

C	C	C	C	C	C	C	C

C	C	C	C				
				C	C	C	C

C	C				C	C	
		C	C				C	C

Sun & Moon

Written by Lee D. Stockner
Translated & Arranged for Occupational Octaves™ by Lee D. Stockner

C	C	C	→				
				C	C	C	→

C	→			C	→	→	→
		C	→				

C		C		C	→	→	→
	C		C				

	C		C				
C		C		C	→	→	→

Published by Music Lee Inclined Guy, Inc

Pg. 2

The New D

Written by Lee D. Stockner
Translated & Arranged for Occupational Octaves™ by Lee D. Stockner

C	→	→	→	D	→	→	→

C	→	D	→	C	→	D	→

C	D	C	D	C	D	C	D

C	C	C	C				
				C	C	C	C

Published by Music Lee Inclined Guy, Inc

Seedy Song

Traditional
Translated & Arranged for Occupational Octaves™ by Lee D. Stockner

C	C	C	C	D	D	D	D

C	C	C	C	D	D	D	D

C	D	D	→	D	C	C	→

C	D	C	D	C	→	→	→

Published by Music Lee Inclined Guy, Inc.

Hand Switch

Written by Lee D. Stockner
Translated & Arranged for Occupational Octaves™ by Lee D. Stockner

	D		D	→			
C		C			C	C	→

D		D			D	D	→
	C		C	→			

			D	D	D		D
C	C	C				C	

D	→	→					
			C	C	→	→	→

Published by Music Lee Inclined Guy, Inc.

The New E

Written by Lee D. Stockner
Translated & Arranged for Occupational Octaves™ by Lee D. Stockner

C	C	D	D	E	E	D	D

C	C	D	D	E	E	D	D

E	C	E	→	D	E	C	→

C	C	D	E	C	E	C	→

Published by Music Lee Inclined Guy, Inc.

Mary Had a Little Lamb

Traditional
Translated & Arranged for Occupational Octaves™ by Lee D. Stockner

E	D	C	D	E	E	E	→

D	D	D	→	E	E	E	→

E	D	C	D	E	E	E	C

D	D	E	D	C	→	→	→

Eureka

Written by Lee D. Stockner
Translated & Arranged for Occupational Octaves™ by Lee D. Stockner

C	D	E	C	C	D	E	C

E	→	D	→	C	→	→	→

C	D	E	C	C	D	E	C

D	→	E	→	C	→	→	→

Published by Music Lee Inclined Guy, Inc.

Bouncing Around

Written by Lee D. Stockner
Translated & Arranged for Occupational Octaves™ by Lee D. Stockner

E	→	→	C	D	→	C	→

E	→	→	C	D	→	C	→

C	→	→	→	D	→	→	→

E	E	D	D	E	C	C	→

The New B

Written by Lee D. Stockner

Translated & Arranged for Occupational Octaves™ by Lee D. Stockner

C	→	→	→	B	→	→	→

C	B	C	B	C	→	C	→

C	→	→	→	B	→	→	→

C	B	C	B	C	→	C	→

Published by Music Lee Inclined Guy, Inc.

Pinball

Written by Lee D. Stockner
Translated & Arranged for Occupational Octaves™ by Lee D. Stockner

	D		E		D		E
B		C		B		C	

	D				E	→	→	→
B		C	B					

	D		E		D		E
B		C		B		C	

	D	E	D				
B				C	→	→	→

Published by Music Lee Inclined Guy, Inc.

The New A

Written by Lee D. Stockner
Translated & Arranged for Occupational Octaves™ by Lee D. Stockner

				E	E	C	C
A	A	C	C				

		D	D	E	E	D	D
B	B						

E	D	C				E	C
			B	A	C		

E	D						
		C	B	A	→	→	→

Published by Music Lee Inclined Guy, Inc.

Skip & Jump

Written by Lee D. Stockner
Translated & Arranged for Occupational Octaves™ by Lee D. Stockner

E	E	E	D	C	C	C	
							B

A	A	A	B	C	→	→	→

E	E	E	D	C	C	C	
							B

A	A	A	B	A	→	→	→

Published by Music Lee Inclined Guy, Inc.

The New F

Written by Lee D. Stockner
Translated & Arranged for Occupational Octaves™ by Lee D. Stockner

C	→	→	D	→	→	E	D	C			D
									B	C	

E	→	→	C	→	→						
						A	→	→	C	→	→

F	F	F	F	E	D				C	→	→
						A	B	C			

						D	C	→	→	→	→	→
A	→	→	B	C							

Published by Music Lee Inclined Guy, Inc.

The New g

Written by Lee D. Stockner
Translated & Arranged for Occupational Octaves™ by Lee D. Stockner

C	D	E	F				
				C	B	A	g

C	C	D	E	C	→		
						B	g

C	B	A	g	C	B	A	g

A	A	B	B	C	→	→	→

Published by Music Lee Inclined Guy, Inc.

Pg. 15

Yankee Doodle (EZ)

Traditional
Translated & Arranged for Occupational Octaves™ by Lee D. Stockner

C	C	D	E	C	E	D	
							g

C	C	D	E	C	→		
						B	g

C	C	D	E	F	E	D	C

						C	→
B	g	A	B	C	→		

Published by Music Lee Inclined Guy, Inc.

Pg. 16

Twinkle, Twinkle, Little Star (EZ)

Traditional
Translated & Arranged for Occupational Octaves™ by Lee D. Stockner

		D	D	E	E	D	→				
g	g							C	C	B	B

				D	D	C	C				
A	A	g	→					B	B	A	→

D	D	C	C							D	D
				B	B	A	→	g	g		

E	E	D	→								
				C	C	B	B	A	A	g	→

Published by Music Lee Inclined Guy, Inc.

There Was an Old Woman

Traditional
Translated & Arranged for Occupational Octaves™ by Lee D. Stockner

					C	C	C		D	D	D	→
g	g	C	C				A					

D									C	C	C	→
	g	B	B	B	A	B	g					

C				C	→	C		D	D	D	→
	g	C	C				A				

D							D	C	C	C	→
	g	B	B	B	A	B					

Published by Music Lee Inclined Guy, Inc.

A Few More Things to Learn:

Chords: Pushing on notes at the same time makes musical harmonies and amazing sounds! Chords are two or more notes played at the same time with one or both hands. In Lee Stockner's Music Box Method, chords are displayed like this:

The chords are played like this:

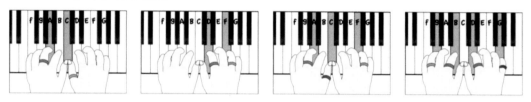

The Black Dots and the Black Notes: The piano is made up of white keys and also many black keys. A black dot on the upper right or left side of a letter means to push on a black key:

When the black dot is on the upper right side of a letter, play the black note to the right.

When the black dot is on the upper left side of a letter, play the black dot to the left.

Rests: When there's a rest, a student should let go of the piano and say "REST!" out loud. After the rest, the hands return to the piano to play the next note/chord.

Hot Cross Buns

Traditional
Translated & Arranged for Occupational Octaves™ by Lee D. Stockner

D	→	C	→				
				•B	→	→	→

D	→	C	→				
				•B	→	→	→

				C	C	C	C
•B	•B	•B	•B				

D	→						
		C	→	•B	→	→	→

Published by Music Lee Inclined Guy, Inc.

Pg. 20

Here Comes the Chord

Written by Lee D. Stockner
Translated & Arranged for Occupational Octaves™ by Lee D. Stockner

C	D	E				C	C		C	→	→
			C	B	A			B			

C	D	E							C	D	→	→
			C	B	A	B	→				

E	D	C					C	→	→		
			C	B	A				B	→	→

C	E	C					E / C	→	→	→	→	→
			A	C	A							

Published by Music Lee Inclined Guy, Inc.

Singing Tune

Written by Lee D. Stockner
Translated & Arranged for Occupational Octaves™ by Lee D. Stockner

				F	→	→	C
A	→	→	C				

			D	F	→	→	D
•B	→	→					

				D	→		
•B	→	C	→			A	→

		D	E	F	→	→	→
C	•B						

Published by Music Lee Inclined Guy, Inc.

Call & Respond

Written by Lee D. Stockner
Translated & Arranged for Occupational Octaves™ by Lee D. Stockner

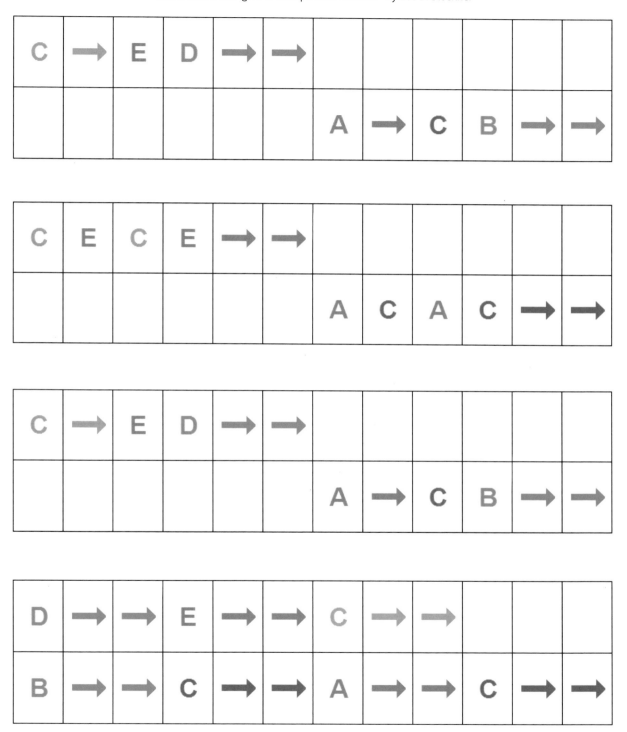

Published by Music Lee Inclined Guy, Inc.

Rainy Day

Written by Lee D. Stockner
Translated & Arranged for Occupational Octaves™ by Lee D. Stockner

A	C	B	→	A	C	B	→

							C E → →
A	B	C	B	A	→		

A	C	B	B	A	C	B	→

							C E → →
A	A	C	B	A	→		

The Doorbell is Ringing

Traditional
Translated & Arranged for Occupational Octaves™ by Lee D. Stockner

E	C	D						D	E	C	→	→
			g	→	→	g						

E	D	C						D	E	C	→	→
			g	→	→	g						

C	→	→				C	→	→	E	→	→
			g	→	→	g	→	→	C	→	→

Published by Music Lee Inclined Guy, Inc.

Mountain Tops

Written by Lee D. Stockner
Translated & Arranged for Occupational Octaves™ by Lee D. Stockner

	C	F	C		C	E	C
A				A			

	C	F	C				D
A				A	→	→	

		C	D	E	F	E	→
A	B						

F	E	D	C			C E	→ →
				A	→		

Published by Music Lee Inclined Guy, Inc.

Tennis Match

Written by Lee D. Stockner
Translated & Arranged for Occupational Octaves™ by Lee D. Stockner

	C	E		C	E			F			F
g			g			A	C		A	C	

	C	E		C	E			E			E
g			g			g	B		g	B	

C	→	→	E	→	→	F	→	→	C	→	→
g	→	→			C	→	→				

C	D	F	E	→	→	E	→	→	E	→	→
					B	→	→	C	→	→	

Published by Music Lee Inclined Guy, Inc.

The New G

Written by Lee D. Stockner

Translated & Arranged for Occupational Octaves™ by Lee D. Stockner

C	E	G		C	E	G	→
			g				

		D	D	G	→	→	→
g	B						

					D	C	E
g	B	A	C	B			

D	E	G	E	C	→	→	→

Published by Music Lee Inclined Guy, Inc.

Row Your Boat (EZ)

Traditional
Translated & Arranged for Occupational Octaves™ by Lee D. Stockner

g	→	→	g	→	→	g	→	A	B	→	→

				C	D	→	→	→	→	→	
B	→	A	B	→							

G	G	G	D	D	D						
						B	B	B	g	g	g

D	→	C									
			B	→	A	g	→	→	→	→	→

Published by Music Lee Inclined Guy, Inc.

The Rest Song

Written by Lee D. Stockner
Translated & Arranged for Occupational Octaves™ by Lee D. Stockner

C	D	E	G	F	E	D	
							C

							𝄽
B	g	A	B	C	→	→	𝄽

C	D	E	G	F	E	D	
							C

							𝄽
B	g	A	B	C	→	→	𝄽

Published in 2019 by Music Lee Inclined Guy, Inc.

Just Relax

Written by Lee D. Stockner
Translated & Arranged for Occupational Octaves™ by Lee D. Stockner

		E	→			D E	⇉
A	→	C	→	B	→		

			D	E			
A	B	C			C	A	→

		E	→			D E	⇉
A	→	C	→	B	→		

	D	→		E	→	→	→
B			B	A C	⇉	⇉	⇉

Published by Music Lee Inclined Guy, Inc.

Shepherd's Song

Written by Ludwig van Beethoven
Translated & Arranged for Occupational Octaves™ by Lee D. Stockner

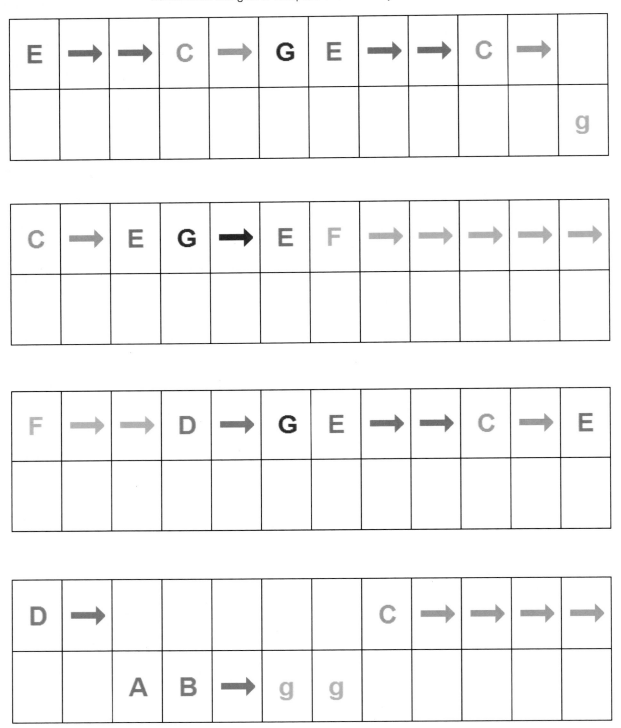

Published by Music Lee Inclined Guy, Inc.
Pg. 32

The New f

Written by Lee D. Stockner
Translated & Arranged for Occupational Octaves™ by Lee D. Stockner

C	B	A	g	f	A	g	→

f	g	A	B	C	→	C	→

C	B	A	g	f	A	g	g

E	F	D	F	C	E	C	→

Wheels on the Bus (EZ) – Pg. 1

Traditional
Translated & Arranged for Occupational Octaves™ by Lee D. Stockner

						D	→
B•	→	B•	B•	B•	→		

F	→	D	→				
				B•	→	→	→

C	→						
		A	→	f	→	→	→

F	→	D	→				
				B•	→	f	→

Published by Music Lee Inclined Guy, Inc.

Wheels on the Bus (EZ) – Pg. 2

Traditional
Translated & Arranged for Occupational Octaves™ by Lee D. Stockner

Published by Music Lee Inclined Guy, Inc.

A Little Night Music (EZ) – Pg. 1

Written by Wolfgang Amadeus Mozart

Translated & Arranged for Occupational Octaves™ by Lee D. Stockner

Published by Music Lee Inclined Guy, Inc.

A Little Night Music – Pg. 2

Written by Wolfgang Amadeus Mozart
Translated & Arranged for Occupational Octaves™ by Lee D. Stockner

D	C	C	→	𝄽	E	D	C	C			
				𝄽					B	B	→

𝄽	D	F		C	→	→		C	→	→	
𝄽		B				g					g

C		C	E	C	→	→	→	
	g							

Published by Music Lee Inclined Guy, Inc.

The Occupational Octaves Piano™ Family of Products:

Occupational Octaves Piano, Books 1-8,
available at OccupationalOctaves.com

Books 1-8, Pop Music, Classical Music, and Book Supplements,
digitally available at SheetMusicPlus.com

The Occupational Octaves™ Cloud Platform for Professionals,
available at MundoPato.com/OccupationalOctaves

The curriculum is intended for a variety of professionals and includes over 500 trackable goals and data points that instructors can target in numerous therapeutic and educational environments. These targets range from fine motor movement to concentration to self-expression and, with UnitusTI, progress is easy to visualize through reports and charts. Occupational Octaves Piano™ is also "Non-Music-Instructor-Friendly," meaning instructors without a music background will have equal success in program implementation.

- Music Education
- Occupational Therapy
- Assisted Living/Aging in Place

- Special Education
- DIY Piano
- Quality of Life/Flow State

- Music Therapy
- Parents/Families
- Various Therapies